· AARON BLABEY ·

the BAD GUYS

EPISODE

15

OPEN WIDE
AND
SAY ARRRGH!

D1620844

Pssst!

Hey, Wolfie . . .

KU-336-850

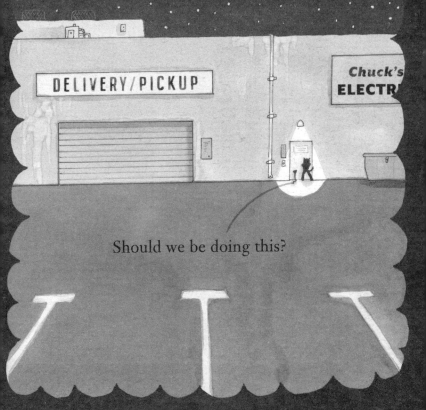

MMMUURRGH!

• CHAPTER 1 •

THE DENTAL APPOINTMENT

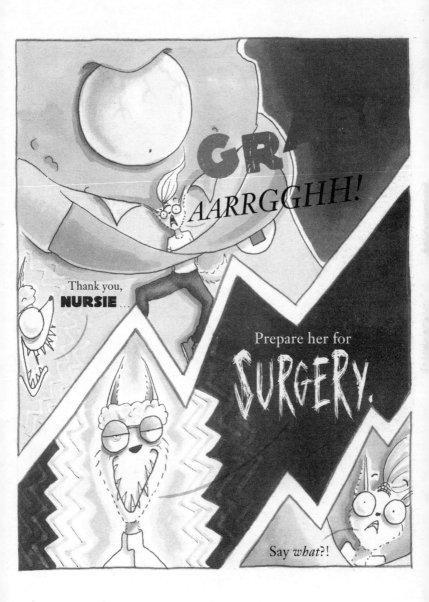

Ohhhhh, silly me!
It's pronounced
THE ONE!

AS IN **THE ONE** WHO IS **HAREBRAINED** ENOUGH TO THINK SHE CAN CHALLENGE THE MAGNIFICENT...

Am I saying that right now?
The One?

GREAT!

Well, young lady,

DELUSIONAL
AMBITIONS

are all well and good,
but they won't help you much
if you don't take care of your . . .

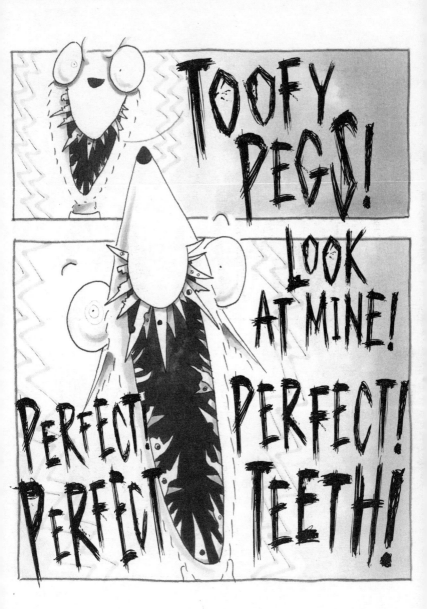

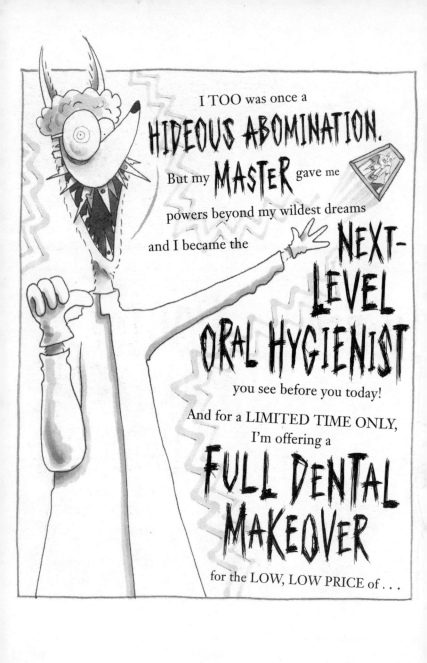

JUST HEARING YOU SCREAM.

BUT WAIT! THERE'S MORE!

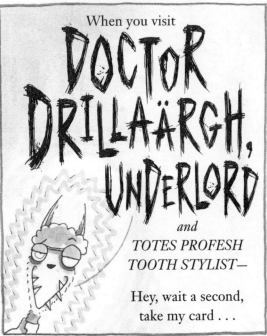

When you visit

DOCTOR DRILLAÄRGH, UNDERLORD

and

TOTES PROFESH TOOTH STYLIST—

Hey, wait a second, take my card . . .

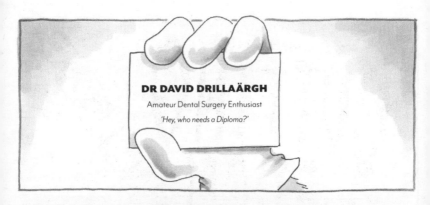

Well, GO ON!
It's not going to
re-fuel itself.

And no stopping for snacks!

Lollipop?

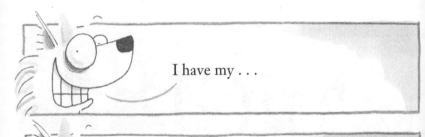

I have my . . .

. . . moments.

DRILL!

· CHAPTER 2 ·
BAIT

The only thing we have going for us is the **ELEMENT OF SURPRISE.**

If **SNAKE** sees us coming, we're done for.
And **FOX** isn't here to help us this time.

If he gets us, we're *his*.

For good.

I sure hope that little guy is OK.

I was eating out one night . . .

... when this little guy came out of nowhere
and started screaming that I'd stolen his meal.

I informed him that he was mistaken.

He considered this for a moment
. . . and then said,

'Sure, chico. You have
that little entrée.
You've put me in the
mood for . . .'

A MAIN COURSE.

What a beautiful story.

HEY, LOOK!
IS THAT . . . ?

IT'S HIM!

OK.
This is our one chance.
Let's grab him fast.

And don't forget, this is
all about the element of . . .

• CHAPTER 3 •
THE UTENSIL WITHIN

49

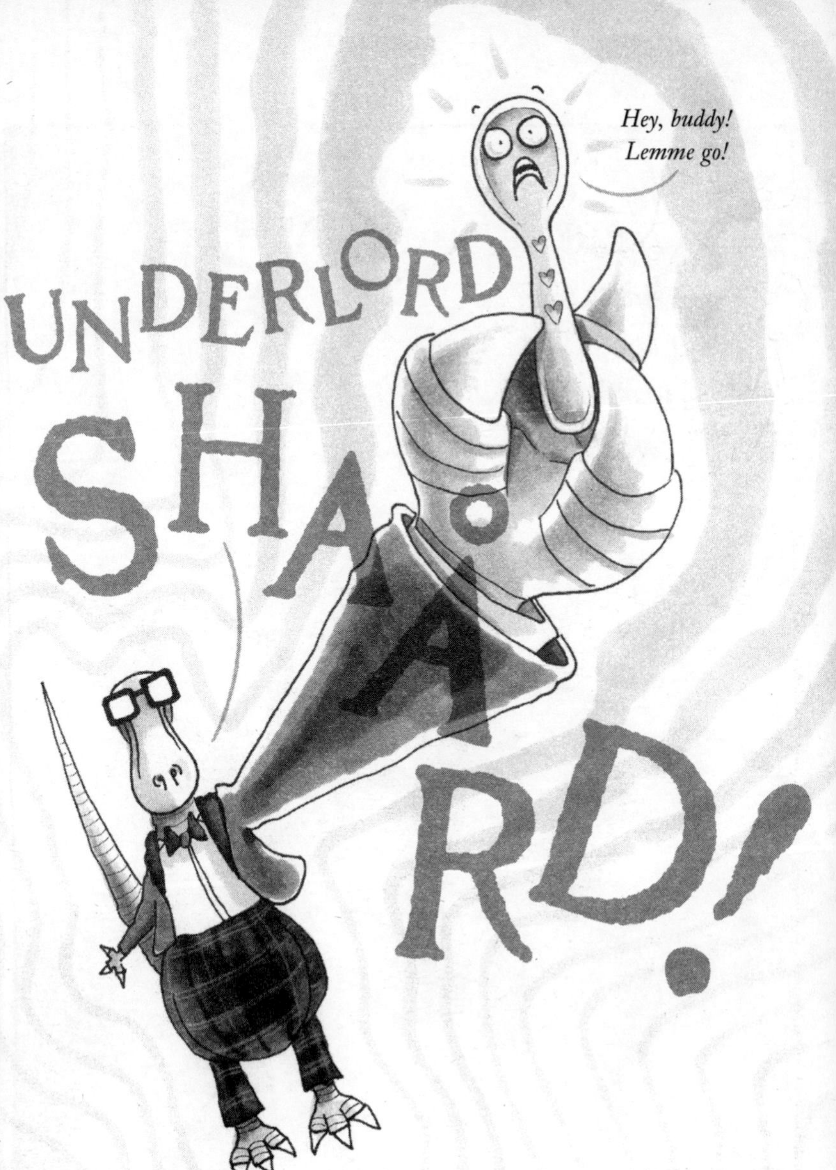
Hey, buddy!
Lemme go!
UNDERLORD
SHAAARD!

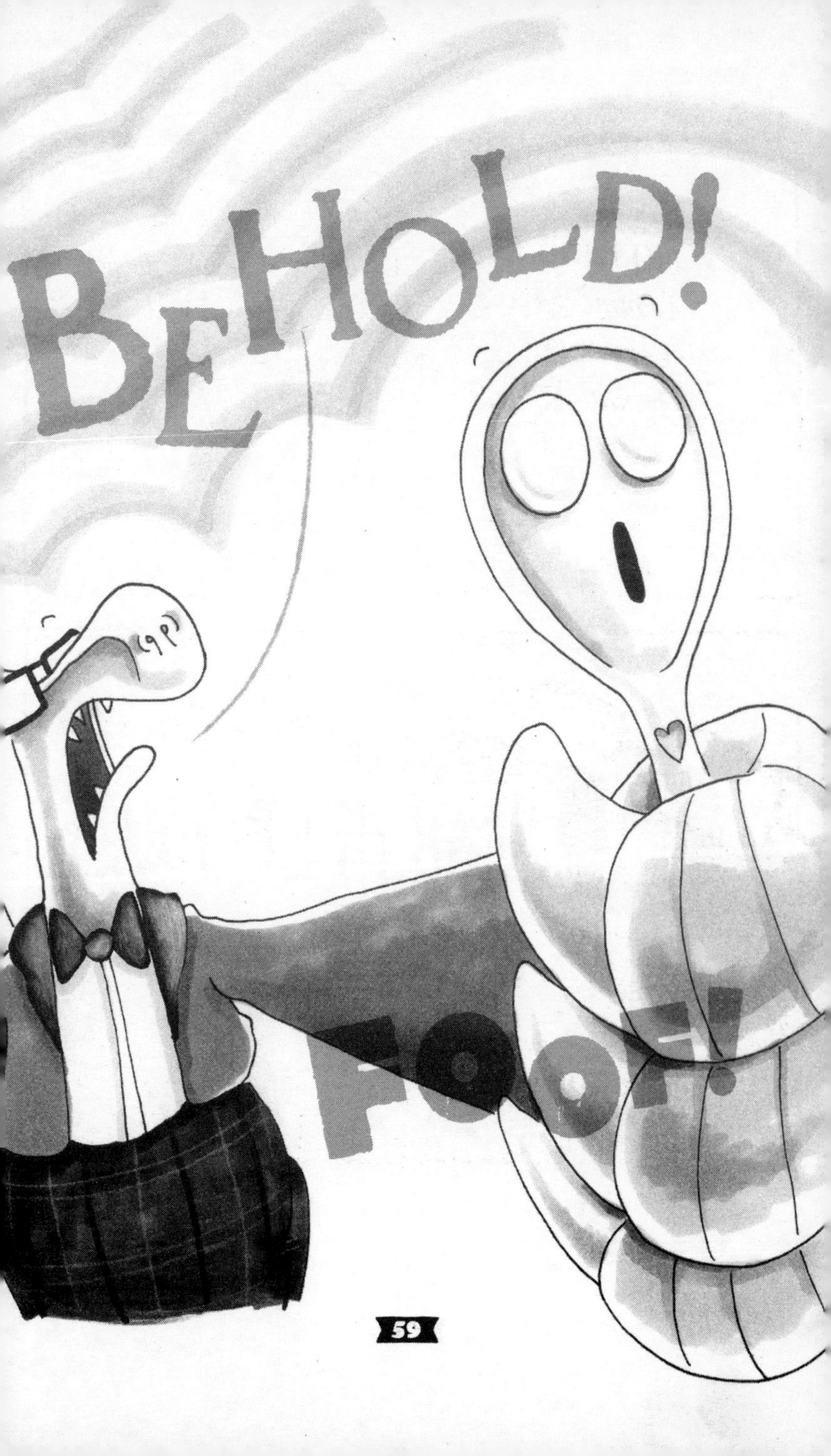
BEHOLD!
FOOF!

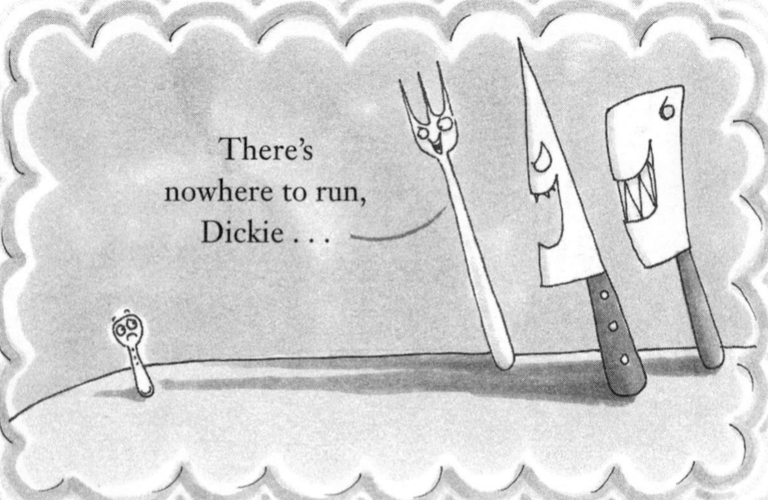
There's
nowhere to run,
Dickie . . .

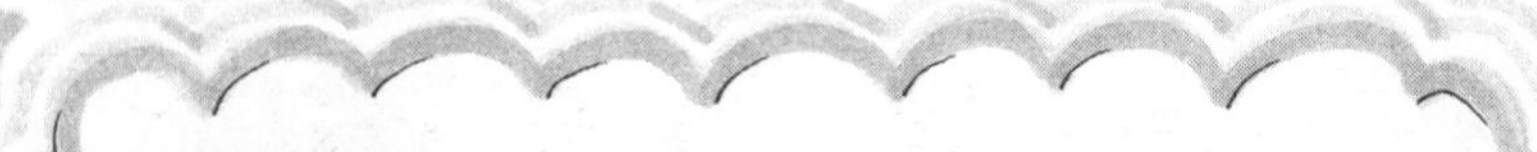
I CAN HELP YOU...

Dang . . .

Wait . . . what?!
He's just . . . a
BABY SPOON?!

Called 'Dickie'?

Dang . . .

And his whole universe is
populated by **UTENSILS?**

That is, like, SO random . . .

You're missing the point . . .

No, seriously . . .
UTENSILS?!

The POINT is . . .

He's not as scary as he seems!
He's not some unbeatable MONSTER.
He just **LOOKED** like one.

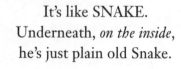

It's like SNAKE.
Underneath, *on the inside*,
he's just plain old Snake.

We can BEAT these guys!

All we have to do is
NOT BE AFRAID
of them.

Hold up.

If any of **US** tried what the dinosaur

just did, we'd be *dead*.

We wouldn't have even made it outside the ship.

And even if we *did* survive being

CRUSHED BY SPACE,

we'd have been

CHOPPED

TO PIECES.

What just happened didn't

make any sense.

We should

TOTALLY

be afraid of them.

Look, I don't know how Milt just did what he did, but it's a *start*, isn't it?

MILT has
POWER
OVER THEM.

Maybe . . .

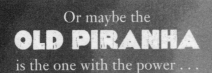

Or maybe the
OLD PIRANHA
is the one with the power . . .

Or *maybe* the power is
actually coming from
SOMEONE ELSE . . .

Dang . . .

· CHAPTER 4 ·

DARK AND WEIRD

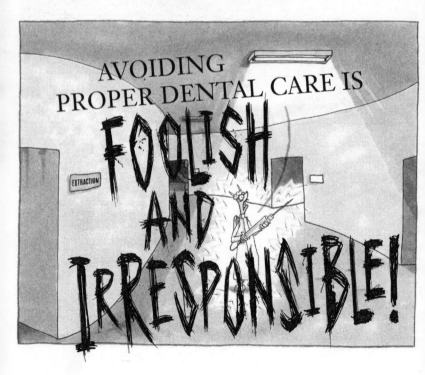

AVOIDING PROPER DENTAL CARE IS

FOOLISH AND IRRESPONSIBLE!

EXTRACTION

And if you think you're not paying for this appointment . . .

NURSIE!
FIND THEM!

A universe ruled by a **PSYCHOTIC DENTIST?!** Does this make any sense to you?

Not really, no.

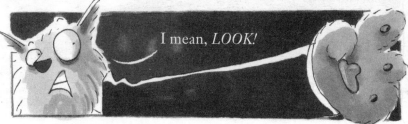

I mean, *LOOK!*

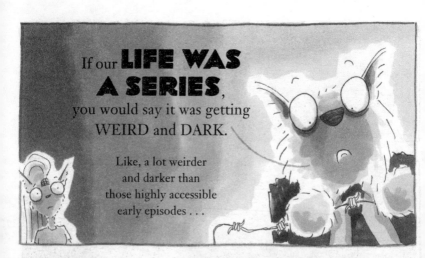

If our **LIFE WAS A SERIES**, you would say it was getting WEIRD and DARK.

Like, a lot weirder and darker than those highly accessible early episodes . . .

It's because we're getting close to . . . *you know who.*

The **HEAVY METAL CENTIPEDE?**

Yes,
I know it sounds strange,
but it's a *good* sign
things are getting scarier . . .

It means he's close.

He's here?! In *this* universe?

I don't think so . . . no.
But we're definitely getting warmer.

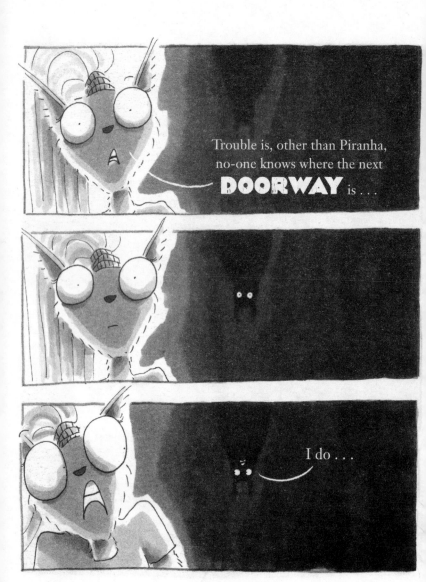

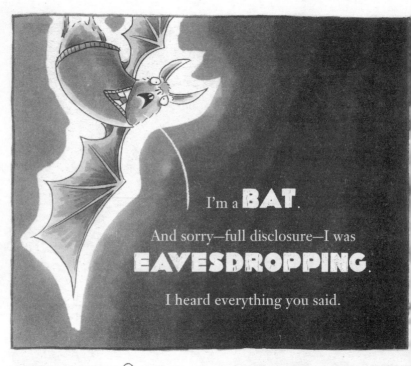

The secret

INTER-DIMENSIONAL DOORWAY

that leads to **HIM?**

Yes, I absolutely know where it is.

100%.

Him?

I CAN HEAR YOU! *WHERE ARE YOU?!*

WE'RE IN THE FLOSS ROOM!

Uh oh. I wish I hadn't said that . . .

He's HORRIBLE. And now he'll find us!

He can't tell a lie and he feels compelled to help others.

Bingo!

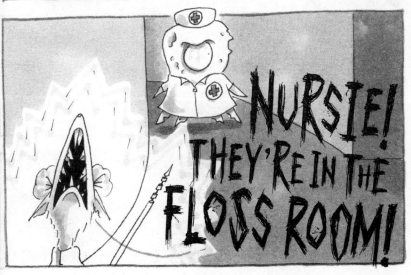

NURSIE! THEY'RE IN THE FLOSS ROOM!

WELL, YES, WE **ARE** ...
BUT WE'RE ABOUT TO
RUN AWAY FROM YOU.
IF YOU HURRY,
YOU'LL
PROBABLY CATCH US
HEADING
TOWARDS THE—

SHHHH!

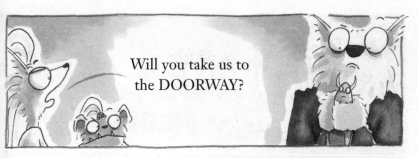

Will you take us to the DOORWAY?

Yes, of course.

But it IS a bit **INCONVENIENT** because I'm meant to be doing **SOMETHING ELSE**.

I'm not trying to make you feel guilty. I just can't hide my feelings and I feel compelled to share them.

Can't help it.

WHAT?!

You seem like the **SLIGHTLY LESS INTELLIGENT MEMBER** of the group.

I deeply regret having said that out loud, but I just . . .

Can't help it.
We get it.

NURSIE! QUICK STICKS!

THIS WAY!

If you're quick, you'll catch us!

Oh no! Now he'll probably catch us!

WHAT IS WRONG WITH YOU?!

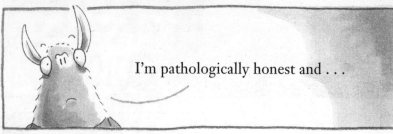

I'm pathologically honest and . . .

WHAT were you supposed to be doing? Instead of taking us to **THE DOORWAY?**

• CHAPTER 5 •
WHO NEEDS MAGIC HANDS?

Oh no . . .

CHICOS!
GET OUT
OF HERE!

Too late for that, *daaaarling* . . .

CRUNCH!

VOOSH!

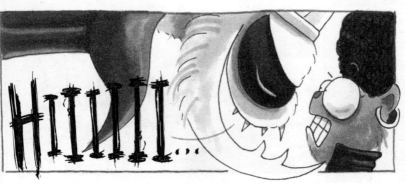

SNAKE!
What is wrong with you, man?!
These are your **FRIENDS!**

THEY **ARE** MY FRIENDS. THAT'S WHY I HAVE A PRESENT FOR THEM...

SHARKIE!
NOOOOO!
FIGHT IT!
THIS IS PERMANENT!

Nnnnnyyyyeah, that beat is *NASTY* . . .

STOP THIS, SNAKE! *STOP THIS!*

YOU GOT A PROBLEM, DO SOMETHING ABOUT IT.

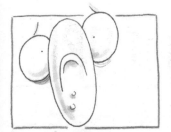

That's what
I thought.

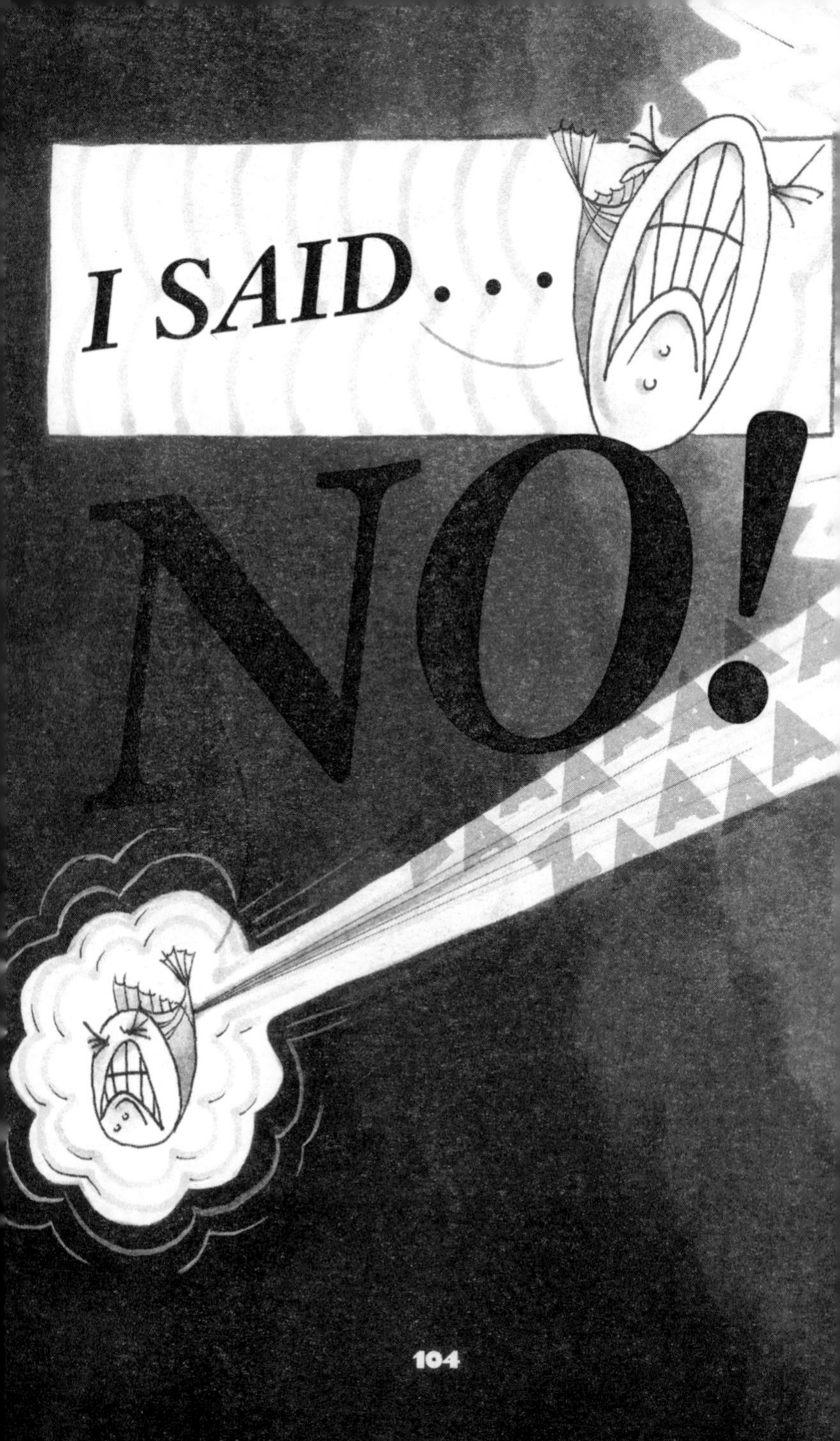
I SAID . . .
NO!

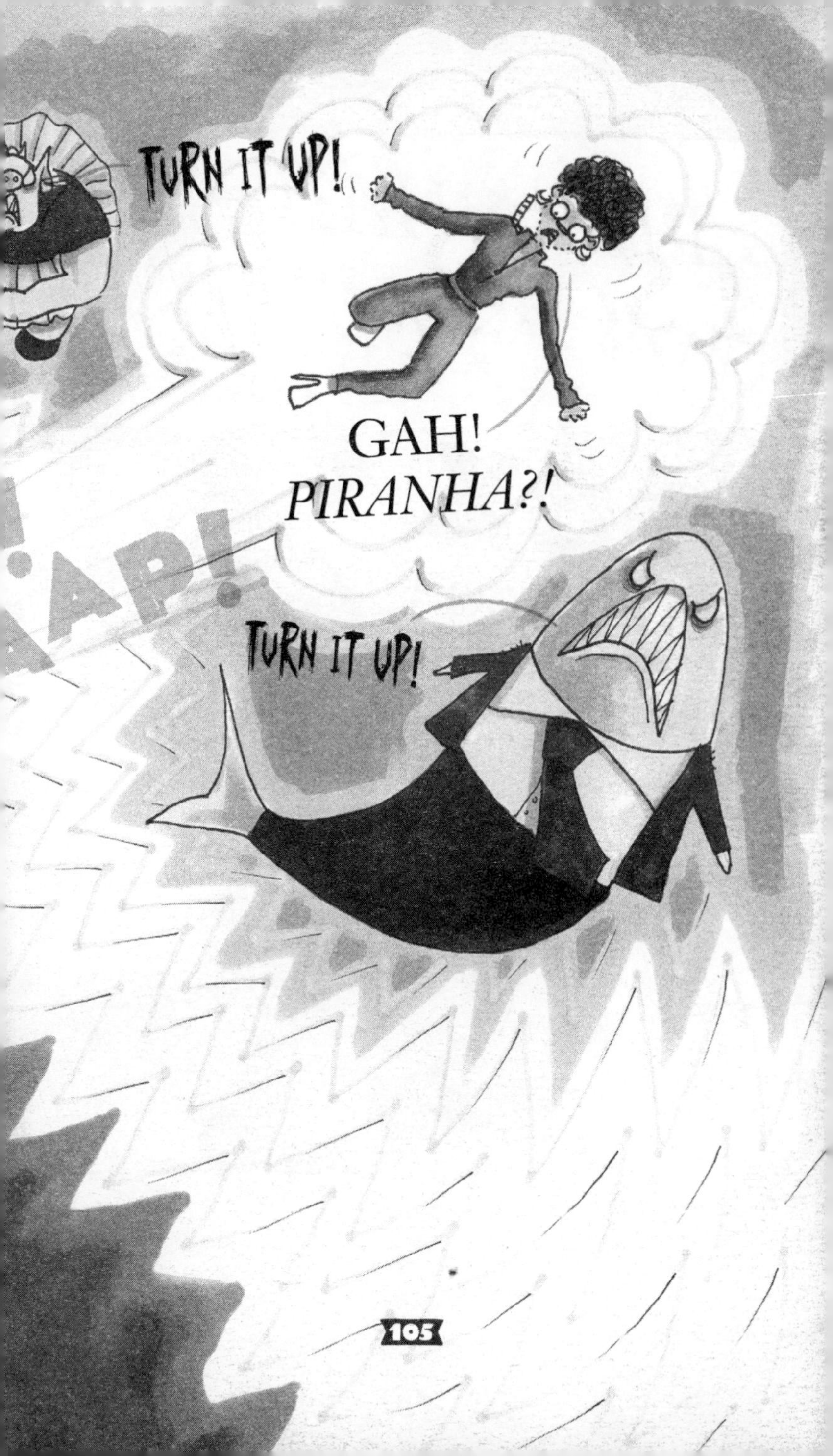
TURN IT UP!
GAH! PIRANHA?!
TURN IT UP!

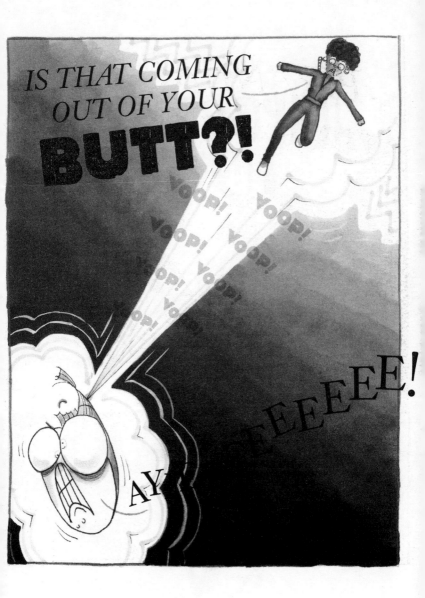

· CHAPTER 6 ·
IMPORTANT, HOW?

And there goes **DICKIE**, the **INTERGALACTIC BABY SPOON.**

If anyone needed proof this is a less important subplot, *there it goes ...*

WRONG!

Shouldn't we try and stop that little spoon guy?

NO!

I mean . . .

You heard the **WEIRD FLOATING LIZARD GUY**— we need to find **THE OTHERS NOW!**

For once, I agree with this idiot . . .

YEAH!

Wait . . .
what?

Let's get to THE OTHERS
RIGHT NOW!

KA-BLART!

· CHAPTER 7 ·

THE TRUTH-TELLER

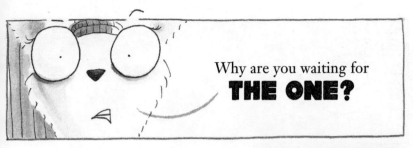

Why are you waiting for
THE ONE?

Ellen . . .

It's OK . . .

*You shouldn't
talk about,
you know . . .
THE ONE.*

How do we know if we can **TRUST** him?

Just letting you know, that as a **BAT**, I rely on my really **QUITE EXCELLENT HEARING** and, accordingly, I can once again hear **EVERYTHING** that you're saying.

Iyyyyyyiiiieeeee . . .
. . . WAS WAITING FOR THE ONE BECAUSE I AM ONE OF THE OTHERS AND THE ONE CAN'T SUCCEED WITHOUT THE OTHERS SO THAT'S WHY I WAS WAITING BUT I SHOULDN'T HAVE SAID THAT BECAUSE I'M ONE OF THE OTHERS.

I'M ONE OF **THE OTHERS.**

WHERE'S THE DOORWAY?!

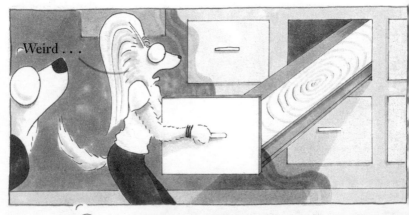

FOOF!

Well, nice to meet you. Good luck with everything.

GRAB!

SLAM!

· CHAPTER 8 ·
ONE AT A TIME, PLEASE

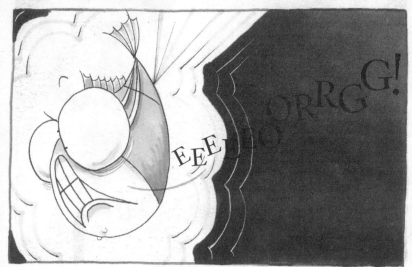

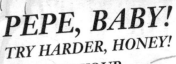

144

YEEEEARGGHH!

I forgot how rad these helicopters are. This is *fun*.

SMACK!

GRRRAAARRGHH!

· CHAPTER 9 ·
THE OTHERS

This is the place?

This is where we find
THE OTHERS?

This is the spot.

Assuming the coordinates
were correct . . .

So . . .

Um . . .

There's nothing here.

YO! WHERE YOU AT?!

Hey, Captain Rando!
Why do you care so much?!

Because he's our **LEADER**
and this means a lot to him.

WHY though?

I don't know, but I'm sure his reasons are **GREAT**.

ARGH, C'MON!

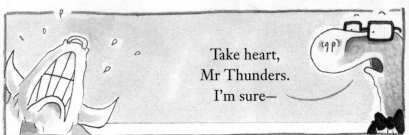

Take heart, Mr Thunders. I'm sure—

Buck?!

Oh, quit yo' fussin' . . .

Y'all can't just turn up **OUT OF THE BLUE** and expect me to be ready at the **DROP OF A HAT.**

Uh . . . I'm sorry . . . Madam. I think there's been some kind of mistake. We're looking for—

Ooooh! **A TASTY TREAT!**

Wha . . . ?!

Keep your hair on, 'Milt'.

MILT?!
How do you know his name?!

Oh, I know *all y'all*.
Been waitin'.
Took you long enough, didn't it?

Wait . . . what?

YOU
are one of THE OTHERS?!

AAAAAARRGHH!

It's cool,
Space Children.

I'm here to blow your minds.

I'm sorry, *who are you?!*

I'm **ZEE**.

And that . . . is **GRANNY**.
You dig?

And you're going to take us to *The Others?*

Not sure I follow . . .

WHERE ARE ALL 'THE OTHERS'?

Sorry, we've come a really long way . . .

If you'd be so kind . . .

we would be so very grateful if you could take us to the

MYSTERIOUS and **LEGENDARY LEGION** of **INTER-DIMENSIONAL SAVIOURS**

known only as

'THE OTHERS'.

We are here to reunite them with

THE ONE.

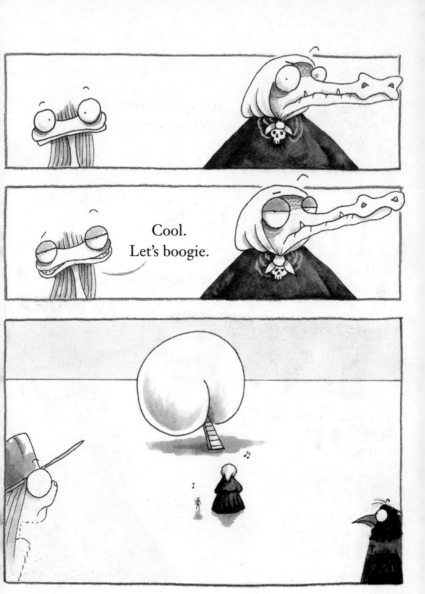

Cool.
Let's boogie.

Hang on . . .

THERE'S ONLY **TWO** OF YOU?!

Who said anything about an army?

And, children, there aren't **TWO** Others . . .

There are **FOUR**.

There's me, **ZEE**.

There's **GRANNY GUMBO JUMBO**.

There's **HONEST ABE**.
Out there, all alone somewhere . . .

Honest . . .
Abe . . .

And then there's . . .
well, you know the
LAST ONE . . .

NO, WE DON'T.
WE REALLY DON'T.

But how could you not?
**YOU BROUGHT
HIM WITH YOU!**

The last of THE OTHERS is . . .

· CHAPTER 10 ·
ABE IN THE WOODS

Oh my.
He's really close now.
Ugh.
I don't feel so good . . .

Me either,
now you mention it.

Oh, that's because of
HER.

HER?
HER, *WHO?*

Oh, she's **BAD**. And when she's around *everything turns bad.*

Wonderful.

Do you know where the next Doorway is?

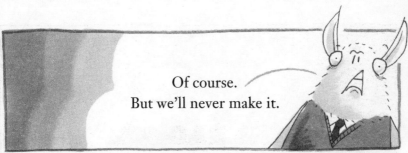

Well, we have to try.

Yep, we do. Absolutely.
I'm all for it.
I'm **ON YOUR SIDE**.

GET DOWN!

EEEEEEEEE!

Everyone
stay
completely
silen—

RE LADY!

WASN'T DOING THIS,
YOU SHOULD KNOW—

WE'RE
RIGHT OVER
HERE!

TO BE CONTINUED...
RIGHT OVER THE PAGE!

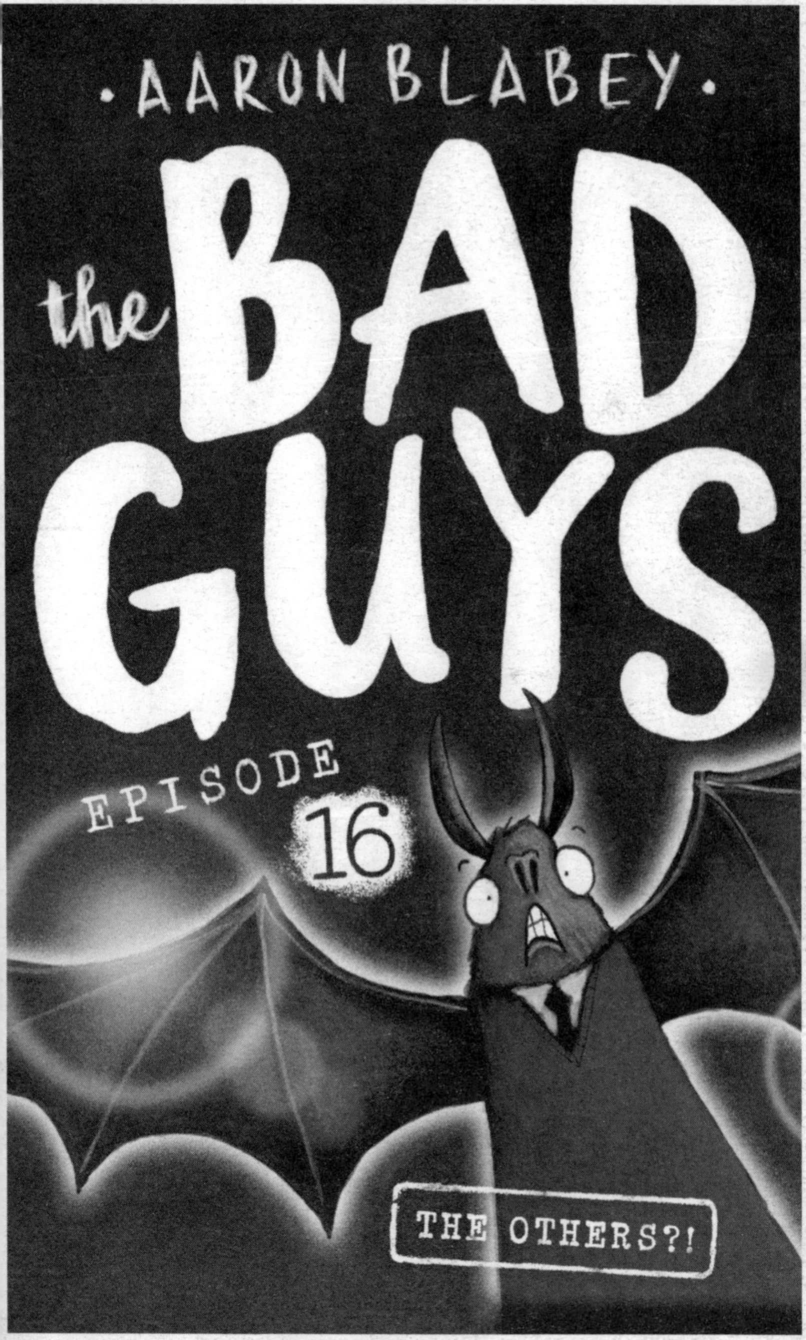

AARON BLABEY
the BAD GUYS
EPISODE 16
THE OTHERS?!

gzzzt!
gzzzt!

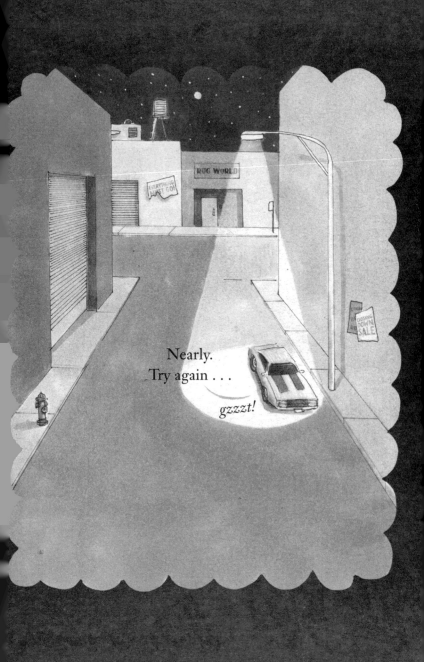

SQUEAL!

Hey, Dad! Check it!

That so?
Moe tells me you've
got talent, kid.

GOOD! MY FAITH IN YOU... IS BEING REWARDED.

WELL DONE, MY CHILD.

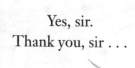

Yes, sir.
Thank you, sir . . .

· CHAPTER 1 ·

THE REALLY BAD LADY

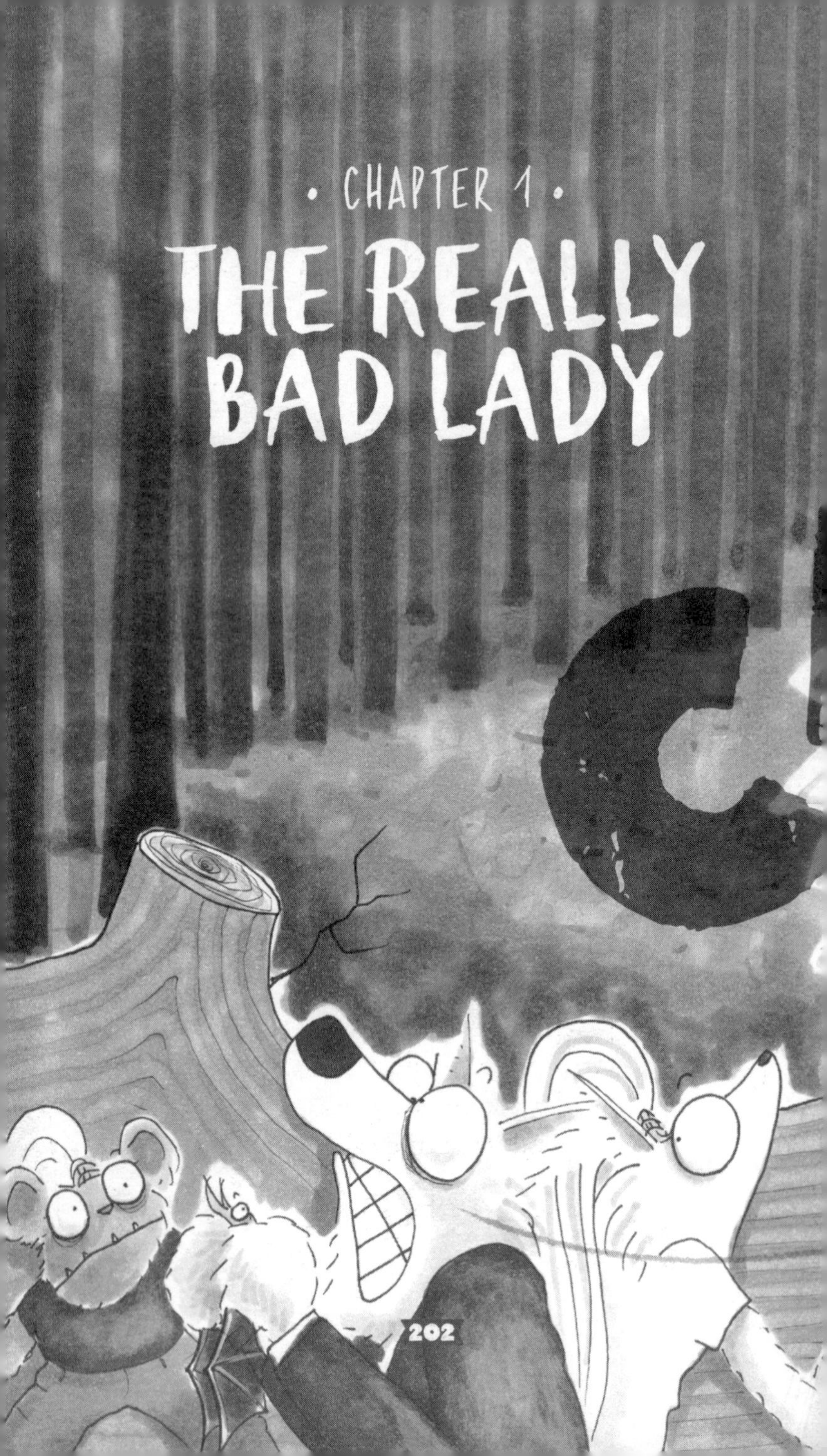

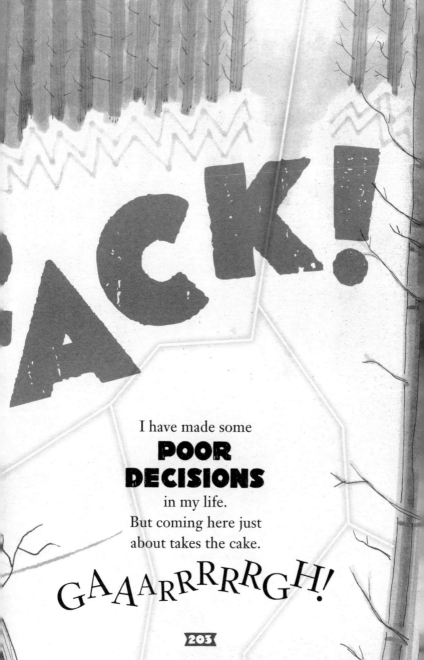

ACK!

I have made some **POOR DECISIONS** in my life. But coming here just about takes the cake.

GAAARRRRRGH!

OK.
I'm afraid I need to talk to Abe,
so get ready—take your hand
away on three . . .

One . . .

two . . .

three!

gasp!

GAAARRGGH!
WHAT IS WRONG
WITH YOU?!

Wolfie!
Chill.

OK, new plan. Abe, could
you just **POINT** the way?
Wolf will gently cover your
mouth and you could just point . . .

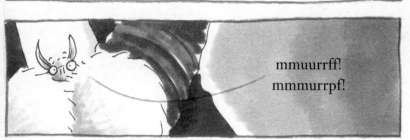

mmuurrff!
mmmurrpf!

It's HER.
She's so *bad* that
she creates
BAD LUCK,
BAD WEATHER,
BAD MOODS
and **BAD HAIR.**

Bad moods?
Come to think of it . . .
maybe that's why I feel so
GROUCHY . . .

217

• CHAPTER 2 •
FORWARD OR BACK?

219

I agree! This is
SHAMEFUL!
Mr Piranha has *never*
run away from a fight!

Are you sure you
can't protect **ALL**
of us with . . .

. . . with . . .

. . . with?

YOUR **MAGIC BUTT?**

Aye! I tried!
It would only hold
ONE OF YOU
at a time.

WHY?!

I don't know.

That's it.
I'm turning us around.
I'm not leaving
SHARK
and I'm not leaving
HOGWILD.
There has to be a way . . .

YEAH!
LET'S DO THAT!

Wait!
What about **AGENT FOX?**
Doesn't she need me?

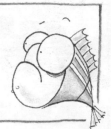

She can't find the
DOORWAYS
without you . . .

This is a nightmare.

WHAT ARE WE GOING TO DO?!

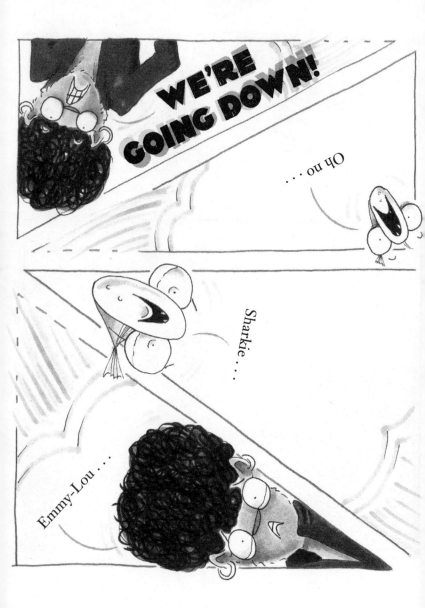

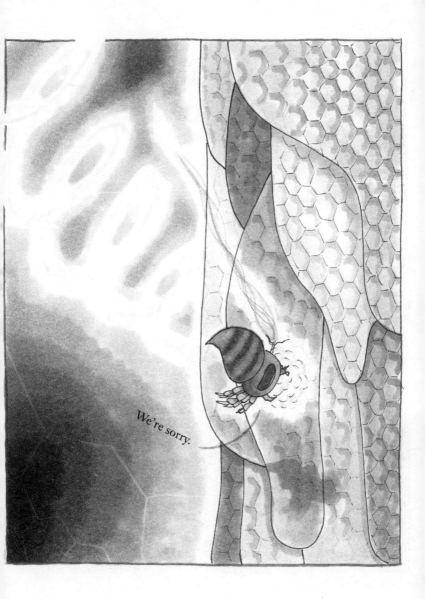

We're sorry.

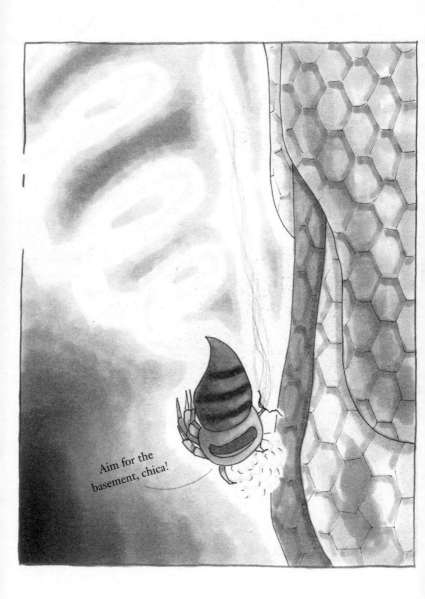

· CHAPTER 3 ·
BULL

You are one of **THE OTHERS?!**

Why on earth didn't you tell us, Mr Thunders? Was it some kind of **TEST?**

YEAH . . .

Well, I think we can safely say that *I* am the only one who passed the test, right Buck?

YEAH!

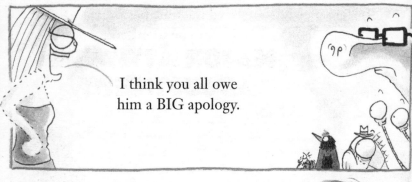

I think you all owe
him a BIG apology.

Wait a minute . . .

YOU TOO, you eight-legged **NERD.** I've heard nothing but **DOUBT** and **SARCASM** and **JEALOUSY** from you two.

You need to *apologise* because it was **OBVIOUS** from the minute **MIGHTY BUCK THUNDERS** stepped into our life that he was a **LEADER,** a **HERO** and an all-round **HUNK OF TOP-SHELF GUY.**

He's certainly very **CONFIDENT.**

That's right!
And what more does
a leader need than
CONFIDENCE?

I don't know,
INTELLIGENCE, maybe?

WISDOM . . .

**INTEGRITY,
COMPASSION,
PEOPLE-SKILLS,
TRUSTWORTHINESS . . .**

I WAS RIGHT . . .

and BUCK THUNDERS
is the
HERO
we've been waiting for.

I mean, **LOOK AT HIM!**
How did you not see it?!
OF COURSE, he's one of
THE OTHERS.

Sorry . . .
who is this guy?

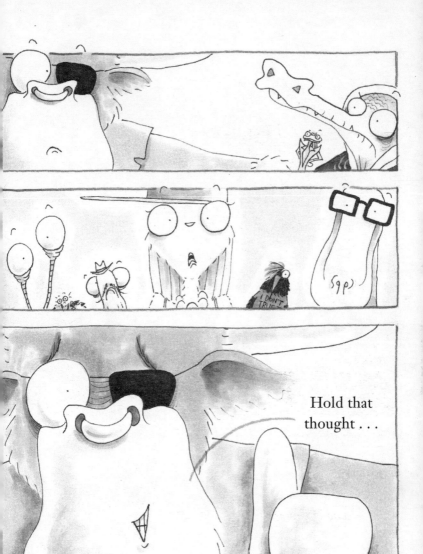

Hold that
thought . . .

WE HAVE TO STOP HIM!

A SPY?!

LET'S GO!

A SPY?!

· CHAPTER 4 ·
THE THING

I'd say this is the place.

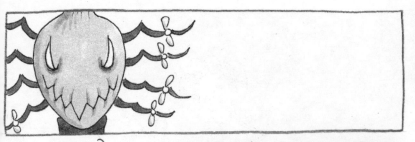

Oh-kay doh-kay . . .

We mean you no harm!
Yaknowwhaddimsayin'?
We are merely . . . weary travellers,
passing through your . . .

beautiful land . . .

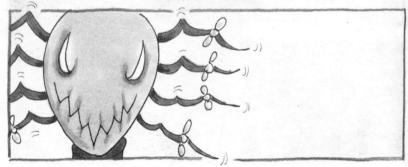

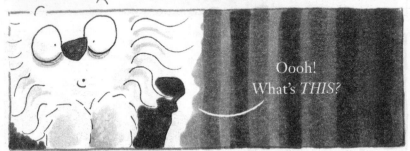

Oooh!
What's *THIS?*

I *really* need to tell you something . . .

Shhh! Hmmm, whatever could this *be*?

What do you need to tell him?

Well, I was going to tell him that this is **UNDERLORD ESMERALDA GHAÂSTLY MOTHER OF NIGHT TERRORS.** I was also going to tell him that she carries a little **ORNATE BOX.** What's more, I was going to tell him that inside that little box is the **MOST FRIGHTENING THING IN THE ENTIRE MULTIVERSE** and if you **LOOK AT IT,** you . . .

INSTANTLY DIE OF FRIGHT.

Do you think I should interrupt and mention it?

Woooooooollllllffffffiiiieeeee . . .

PEEK-A-BOO!

CHAPTER 5 •
WHISTLE STOP

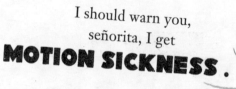

I should warn you, señorita, I get **MOTION SICKNESS . . .**

YOU **FART,** YOU **DIE,** *GOT IT?*

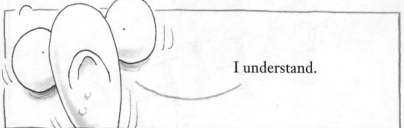

I understand.

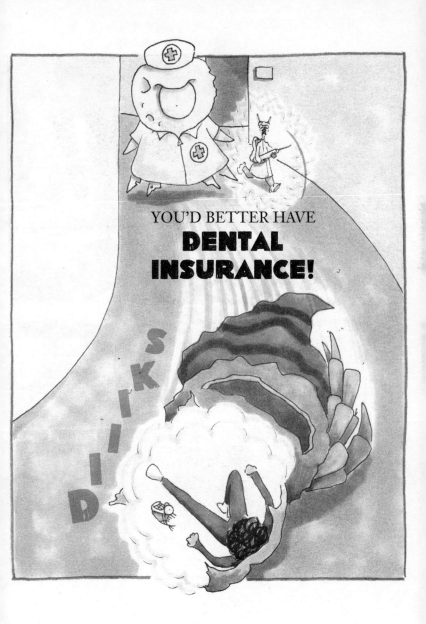

• CHAPTER 6 •

FINALLY, A FEW ANSWERS

Someone has had their **ILLUSIONS SHATTERED.** This will not be pretty.

We'd better choof, groovers.

OK, no.
I'm not going ANYWHERE
until I get some

ANSWERS.

Hiiii-YA!

Woah. Answers to what, birdie?

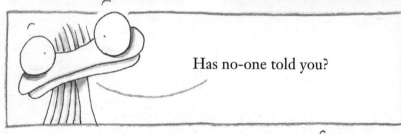

Wow.
That must have been
really frustrating.

YES!

Ain't it obvious?
We're here to help THE ONE.

BUT HOW?

WE **ARE** THE ONE.

What she means is—
We are

PARTS

of THE ONE.

Dig this—

A LOOOOOOOOOOOOONG time ago,

THE ONE

SPLIT HERSELF INTO PARTS

so that the centipede couldn't
get her . . .

She **HID** those parts of herself **AROUND THE MULTIVERSE** to **PROTECT** herself from the centipede.

She **HID THOSE PARTS** until she was ready to *face him*.

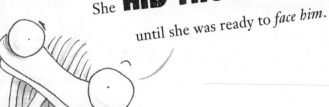

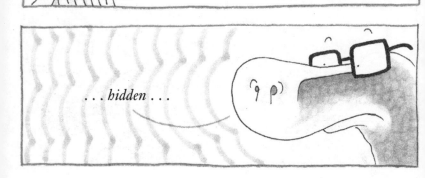

. . . *hidden* . . .

WE ... **ARE** THOSE PARTS. And she's not complete without us.

But NOW, it's time for her to face him, so we need to get back to THE ONE ...

It's time for us to **COMPLETE HER.**

And when you
say 'WE', you mean
YOU,
a really old alligator,
and **HIM,**
the weird little guy,
with the hair.

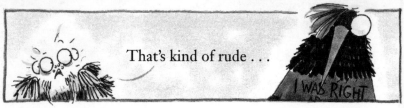

That's kind of rude . . .

What? He's got a
MULLET.
We're all thinking it.

I WAS RIGHT ABOUT IT

It looks good on *him*.

I WAS RIGHT ABOUT

Does it, though?

I WAS RIGHT

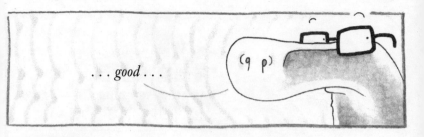

... *good* ...

But how does it work?
Do you just hold hands
with THE ONE and
she's 'complete' again?

Not quite, missy.
Close, but not quite.

We'll explain on the way.
You need to get us there
**BEFORE IT'S
TOO LATE.**

 Without us,
THE ONE WILL FAIL.

 *. . . without us, The One will fail . . .*

 Are you OK, Milt? You're acting kind of weird . . .

 CRASH!

Fluffit! Have you got it out of your system? **WE NEED TO GO!**

I guess not . . .

I WAS RIGHT ABOUT

· CHAPTER 7 ·
OVER AND OUT

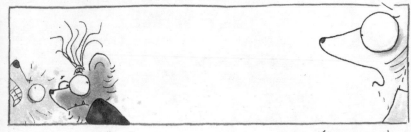

NOOOOO!

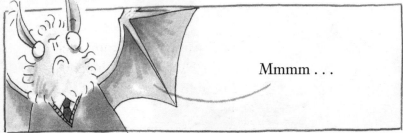

Mmmm . . .

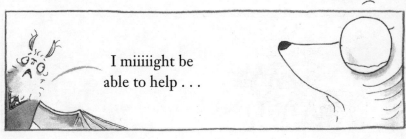

I miiiiight be able to help . . .

REALLY?! PLEASE! PLEASE HELP HIM!

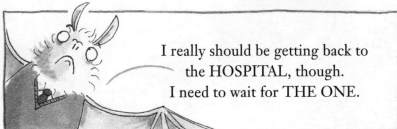

I really should be getting back to the HOSPITAL, though. I need to wait for THE ONE.

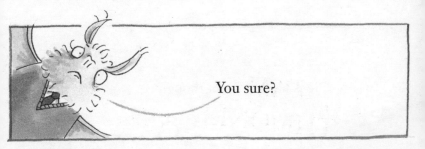

You sure?

Yes, yes,
I'm The One.
And you said that
you're one of
The Others, right?
**AREN'T
THE OTHERS
SUPPOSED
TO HELP ME?**

Well, I guess if you *are*
The One . . .

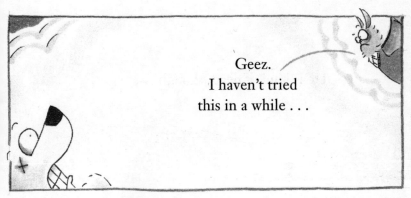

Geez.
I haven't tried
this in a while . . .

BWARP!
BWARP!
BWARP!

Ohhh . . . my . . . g . . .

Wolfie?

Fox?

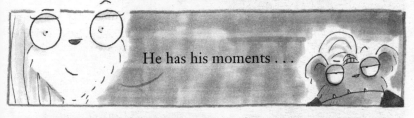

It's The Doorway . . .

We have to jump into **THAT?!** That's impossible!

He wants us to *think* it's impossible.

We just have to **BELIEVE** it's not.

Wait for me!

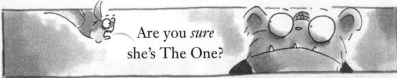

Are you *sure* she's The One?

GRAB!

THUD!

· CHAPTER 8 ·
TIFFANY'S EPIPHANY

SUCCESS!

GOOD LOOKS!

LUXURY BRANDS!

LIFE WAS SIMPLE. **I KNEW WHO I WAS.**

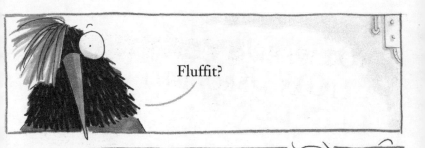

Fluffit?

HE'S NOT A HERO, IS HE?

No, but we kind of have more important things to deal with right now.

NO, YOU'RE NOT A HERO . . .

YOU'RE JUST A COWARDLY LITTLE SPY.

A FAKE!

A PHONEY!

Fluffit, you're at a 10.
We need you at a 2.

I WAS RIGHT

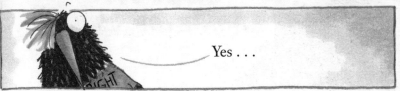

I'm not sure I do . . .

I'M A PHONEY TOO!
I'M NO BETTER THAN **THIS GUY!**

I WAS RIGHT ABOUT BUCK

MY REAL NAME ISN'T **TIFFANY FLUFFIT!** I MEAN, WHO'S CALLED **TIFFANY FLUFFIT?!** SERIOUSLY?!

SNAP!

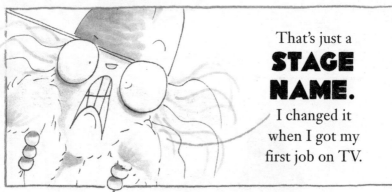

That's just a **STAGE NAME.** I changed it when I got my first job on TV.

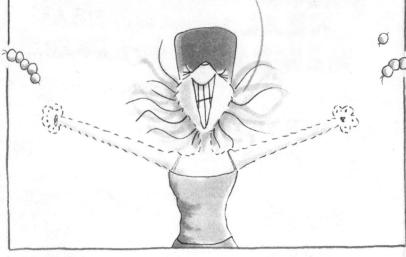

DELORES GRISTLEWURST!

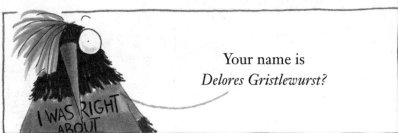

Your name is *Delores Gristlewurst?*

I WAS RIGHT ABOUT

YES, IT IS!

And you know what?

I'm **PROUD** to be DELORES GRISTLEWURST

because DELORES GRISTLEWURST is **REAL!**

DELORES GRISTLEWURST is **NOT A FAKE!**

And DELORES GRISTLEWURST could spot a

PHONEY like
THAT GUY
from a
MILE
AWAY!

She's snapped . . .

DELORES GRISTLEWURST

is the HERO of this story.

AND SO ARE **YOU!** WE ARE **ALL THE HEROES** OF THIS STORY.

I kind of like Delores Gristlewurst.

Ditto.

AND THIS ONE!

AND . . .

Wait . . . didn't you say there's another Other here?

If it's not Buck Thunders . . .

WHO IS IT?

Uh . . . I know this might sound a little odd . . .

but I think it might be **ME** . . .

· CHAPTER 9 ·
A TERRIBLE SHOCK

I need a minute,
por favor . . .

For what?

I need to poop.

Eight years of Med School, for this . . . .

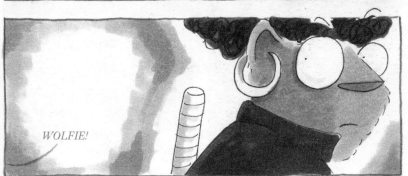

WOLFIE!

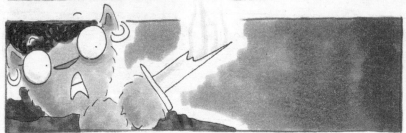

Or BUTTER KNIFE. Whatever you want to call it.

DIDDY WIDDLY!
DIDDY WIDDLY!
DIDDY WIDDLY!
DUGGA
SQUEEEAL!
DUGGA
DUGGA
DIDDY WIDDLY!
DIDDY WIDDL
Wanna HANG OUT?

IN NO WAY GOOD

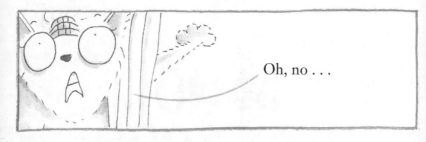

Oh, no . . .

SMACK!

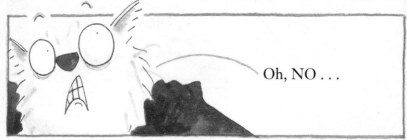

Oh, NO . . .

Oh, yeah . . .

I probably should
have mentioned . . .

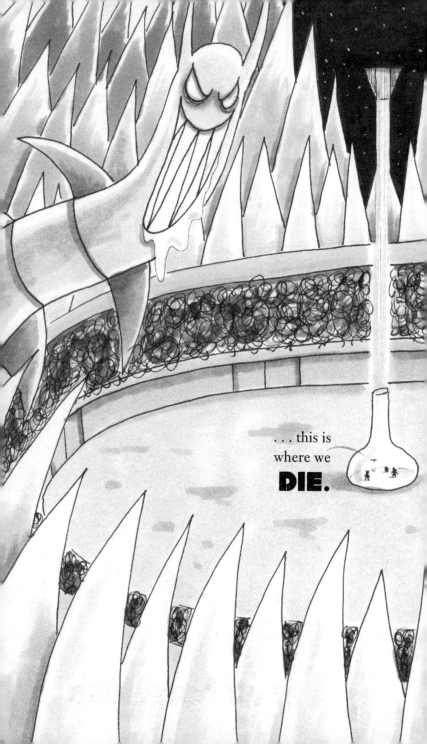